Priority seats

The ACE project
'Literacy for Active Citizenship' series

Written by Foufou Savitzky
Illustrations by Sally Hancox

Priority seats
© Learning Unlimited 2014

Published by Learning Unlimited Ltd as part of the Active Citizenship and Literacy (ACE) project. The ACE project, led by Learning Unlimited, was funded through the European Integration Fund and delivered in partnership with Blackfriars Settlement, Working Men's College and the Institute of Education.

Foreword

The ACE project
'Literacy for Active Citizenship' series

The Active Citizenship and English (ACE) project, led by Learning Unlimited and delivered in partnership with Blackfriars Settlement, Working Men's College and the Institute of Education, received funding from the European Integration Fund (July 2013 to June 2015).

The ACE project aimed to support non-EU women to develop their skills and confidence in English as well as the knowledge and confidence to take an active part in everyday life in the UK. As part of the project we wanted to produce a series of readers for our learners, and other adults also settling in the UK, which include stories about funny, personal and less typical aspects of everyday life in the UK. These books were written by learners and volunteers on the ACE project and the supporting activities have been developed by the Learning Unlimited team.

We hope you enjoy using the 'Literacy for Active Citizenship' series.

To find out more about the ACE project, please see:
www.learningunlimited.co/projects/ace

My name is Foufou and I enjoy
travelling on buses.

When I get the bus to work, I like to find
a seat and read my book.

I don't pay for my travel because I am over 60 years old.

Priority seat

On London buses there are priority seats. These are for people who are disabled, pregnant or elderly. I am not very old but I am over 60 and I like to sit down.

One morning I got on my bus. There were no empty seats and two young men were sitting in the priority seats.

I stood near the priority seats as I hoped one of the young men would offer me a seat. But they didn't so I was a bit annoyed. I thought: "Young men should give their seats to older people like me."

I stared at the young man nearest to me but he did not look at me.

Then I stared at the other young man.
But he did not look at me either because
he was busy reading a book.

After a few stops one of the young men pressed the bell. I was so pleased. Maybe I could sit down at last!

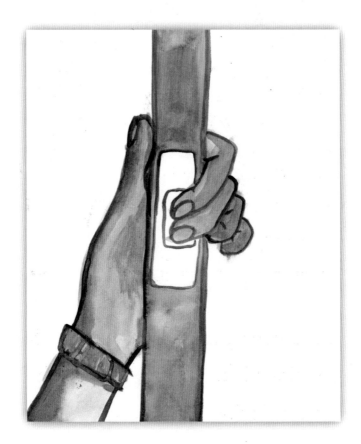

When the young man got up, I saw he
had a white stick. He was blind so he
needed a priority seat.

Then the other young man stood up.
"Good," I thought, "that lazy young
man is getting off as well." Then I saw
that he had two walking sticks. He
had a disability too.

Now I look more carefully at people sitting in priority seats. But I get very cross when I see children sitting there.

Key words

blind	cannot see
cross	angry
disabled	a person with a disability - a problem with their body
pregnant	expecting a baby
priority seats	seats on buses and trains for people who need to sit down for a special reason
stare	look at someone for a long time

Questions

1. Does Foufou pay for her travel? Why? Why not?

2. Who are priority seats for?

3. What happened on the bus?

4. In your country, are there priority seats on buses? Who are they for?

5. What do you say to offer your seat to someone?

6. Describe a bus journey in your country.

Activities

Write a letter or email to a friend at home. Describe a bus journey in the UK.

For more downloadable activities, visit:
www.learningunlimited.co/resources/publications

Acknowledgements

Priority seats was written by Foufou Savitzky and illustrated by Sally Hancox. We are grateful to them for being able to include their work as part of the 'Literacy for Active Citizenship' series.

To find out more about Learning Unlimited, its resources and published materials, CPD and teacher training programmes, project and consultancy work, please see: **www.learningunlimited.co**